The ___game___ was fun.
game jam got

The ape ___ate___ all the nuts.
at age ate

Jane will ___dive___ into the lake.
vine did dive

The bug bit Ron, so Ron got ___mad___.
mad map made

Jake has a hobby. He fixes up vans and sells them.

He finds a big, red van. He waxes it and puts a bike rack on top of it. Then he puts an ice box, a T.V., and a box of games in the back.

"That van looks nice," says his wife.

"We will be sad if you sell it," say his kids.

"This van is not for sale," says Jake. "It's for us."

The bike rack is __on top__ of the van.
on the side   on top
in the back

"This van is for _____," says Jake.
sale   us   bikes

2

Jane's hobby was making bags. The first bag she made was a make-up case for Mom. The case was tan with red dots on it. It had lace on the top, and it zipped up.

"You can carry your make-up in it," Jane said, as she gave Mom the case.

"Thank you," said Mom. "I have wanted a make-up case for ages."

The bag had ten dots.

Mom made a bag for Jane.

Jane made a bag for Mom.

Jane made a bag for Mom.

1, 2, 3, or X?

_1_ The pad has ten pages on it.

_X_ The vane is made of tin.

_3_ The pad has no pages on it.

_2_ Mike takes all ten pages off the pad.

1 First the pad has ten
pages on it.

2 Next

3 Then

4

The tall man's name is _____.

Dave   duck   Jane

Mike can bake a fine _____.

ran   rake   cake

Pat waves to _____.

so   go   Kojo

The pup likes to lick Sal's _____.

face   fine   wide

Ed is racing to get the bus. He is late. He is lugging a big case, so he can't run.

Ed waves as he sees the bus pull up, but the bus driver can't see him, so he takes off.

At first, Ed is mad, but then he says, "It's O.K. I can take a cab."

Ed has a _____.
　　　　buggy　case　van

Ed is _____.
　　late　bug　running

Kojo got a can of ham and six yams. She made baked ham and yams. She made it for Dad.

Dad's face lit up when he had a bite.

"Nice job," he said. "It is yummy!"

Kojo made a ham.

Dad hated the ham.

Kojo licked her lips.

1, 2, 3, or X?

____ Polly takes the cape to Kojo.

____ Polly makes a nice cape.

____ The tape came late.

____ Kojo puts on the cape.

1 First _ _ _ _ _ _ _ _ _ _ _ _ _ _ _

_ _ _ _ _ _ _ _ _ _ _ _ _ _ _ _ _ _

2 Next _ _ _ _ _ _ _ _ _ _ _ _ _ _ _

_ _ _ _ _ _ _ _ _ _ _ _ _ _ _ _ _ _

3 Then _ _ _ _ _ _ _ _ _ _ _ _ _ _ _

_ _ _ _ _ _ _ _ _ _ _ _ _ _ _ _ _ _

Five mice are in a wire _____ .

cage   tag   page

The pin was for _____ .

take   Kate   game

All nine _____ are Nam Min's.

dimes   dims   mad

Penny wants to _____ Pat's pal.

be   by   mess

Miss Ross gave Larry a box of taffy. Larry loved taffy, so he ate it all, five at a time. It was a big box, too!

"Taffy is so yummy," he said, rubbing his tummy.

But then his face got pale, and his tummy got sore.

"Oh, no!" he said. "I think I am sick from all the taffy I ate. I liked it, but I'm sorry I ate it all."

Larry's face got _____.
                    red   puffy   pale

Larry got sick in the _____.
                    face   tummy   den

An ape was sitting on a big rock in his cage. Kate had a bag of nuts by the side of the cage. She tossed five nuts into the cage.

The ape ate up all the nuts, then made a funny face at Kate and patted his tummy.

"You silly ape," said Kate. "Are you saying 'Thank you' or 'More'?"

The ape put nuts on the rock.

Kate made an ape face.

Kate fed nuts to the ape.

1, 2, 3, or X?

____ Jake wins the race with Gus.

____ Jake passes Gus.

____ Jake is in back of Gus.

____ Bill waves "Hi" to Kate.

1 First

2 Next

3 Then

Mom said, "_____, you can't go."

Yes   It   No

Peggy made a name tag for _____.

Taj   hilly   rave

Bem has time to _____.

ride   rid   nine

Jake can ride a _____.

bike   pick   size

A cab driver hops into his cab. He is in a hurry to get to a job.

A tired kitty is taking a nap on the street in back of the cab, but the cab driver can't see her. He is going to back up and drive away.

Rose sees the kitty napping next to the tires of the cab. "Stop!" she yells at the man.

When Rose yells, the cat wakes up, sees the cab, and races off. The lucky cat is saved, thanks to Rose.

The kitty is _____.

              hit   not lucky

                  lucky

The kitty naps in the _____.

             cab   safe   street

Taj made a date to go to the game with Ann. "I'll pick you up at five," he said.

But at five, Taj was home taking a nap. Ann sat and sat, but no Taj.

Then Ann called and woke Taj up.

"I'm sorry I'm late," said Taj in a daze.

Lucky for Taj, the game was late, too, and Ann didn't care.

Taj picks up Ann at six.

Taj is late for the date.

Ann is mad at Taj.

1, 2, 3, or X?

_____ James wiped up the messy tile.

_____ A cab came to get Kate.

_____ Kate called a cab.

_____ Kate got in the cab.

1 First ─ ─ ─ ─ ─ ─ ─ ─ ─ ─ ─ ─ ─

2 Next ─ ─ ─ ─ ─ ─ ─ ─ ─ ─ ─ ─

3 Then ─ ─ ─ ─ ─ ─ ─ ─ ─ ─ ─ ─

The box was for _____.

mop   came   Kate

Dick is late, so he _____.

backs   hi   runs

Wen-Lin came in a _____.

cab   cob   hate

Jan said, "The dime is _____."

age   mane   mine

The man is making a cake with his wife for the first time. He wants to mix it up in a hurry so he can taste it.

"Is it time yet?"

"No, not yet," she tells him. "Take your time." She puts in an egg and she adds a bit of lime to the mix. The man takes a bite of the mix and a big gob of it falls on the rug and makes a mess.

The man's wife isn't happy. "You can make a jug of lime ade, and I'll make the cake!"

The man's wife puts in a bit of _____.

lime   cake   mix

The man takes _____.

a lime   a bite   an egg

Mom and Meg were in the den. "It's time for you to go to bed," Mom said to Meg.

But Meg hated going to bed. "Can't I play a game first?" she said.

"No," said Mom. "You will get too tired if you are up late. Go get into bed, and I will tuck you in. Then you can look at a book if you want to."

It was Meg's bed time.

It was Mom's bed time.

Meg played a game in the den.

1, 2, 3, or X?

_____ The cat hopped on Bem's lap.

_____ The cat napped on Bem's lap.

_____ The kite fell on the ice.

_____ The cat came to Bem.

1 First _ _ _ _ _ _ _ _ _ _ _ _ _

_ _ _ _ _ _ _ _ _ _ _ _ _ _

2 Next _ _ _ _ _ _ _ _ _ _ _ _

_ _ _ _ _ _ _ _ _ _ _ _ _ _

3 Then _ _ _ _ _ _ _ _ _ _ _ _

_ _ _ _ _ _ _ _ _ _ _ _ _ _

The kids _____ in the lake.

hate   wig   wade

Paz has a big red _____.

kite   kick   wide

Betty's dad is so _____.

five   hike   nice

The bus _____ by.

hops   gate   goes

Mom and Dad have a kite for Mike, but Mom says, "Let's not let him see it yet."

"Fine," says Dad, and he hides the kite out back next to a pile of logs.

But the kitty sees the nice, red kite and tugs on it. Dad runs to hide the kite from Mike, but it is too late. Mike sees it.

Dad kids Mike. "The kite is not for you," he tells him. "It's for Mom."

The kitty tugs on ＿＿＿＿＿＿＿.
Mike   the kite
a log

The kite is for ＿＿＿＿＿＿＿.
Mom   Mike
the cat

It's nice and sunny. At first, Jack and Jane are happy playing outside. They ride bikes for miles. Then they play tag on the hill out back.

"Let's have a hopping race. I'll race you to the gate," says Jane. But it is getting hot out.

"I'm too hot, and too tired," Jack tells her. "All I want to do is go in and sit next to the fan for a while. Will you come with me?"

Jane and Jack play a game of jacks.

Jack gets hot and tired.

Jack and Jane hop to the gate.

1, 2, 3, or X?

_____ Dave ate the rice.

_____ Nine mice are in a line.

_____ Dave baked the rice.

_____ The rice was in Dave's tummy.

1 First _ _ _ _ _ _ _ _ _ _ _ _ _ _ _

2 Next _ _ _ _ _ _ _ _ _ _ _ _ _ _ _

3 Then _ _ _ _ _ _ _ _ _ _ _ _ _ _ _

The man's wife _____ limes.

hike   lit   likes

Dad did not make the _____.

cape   is   came

Bem met the man and said "_____."

Hi   Hill   At

James ate the ham he _____.

same   bag   baked

Billy made a nice kite to sell at the kite sale, but his puppy got it and raced off.

By the time Billy got the kite back, he was mad.

"Bad dog!" he said. Billy was tired, too, and he sat down to take a cat nap.

It was time for the kite sale, but Billy was napping. The puppy licked Billy's face and yapped at him. Billy woke up and hugged the puppy. "I'm sorry I got mad at you," he said. "Let's go to the kite sale. But this time I'll carry the kite!"

The puppy _____ Billy.

bit   woke

passed

Billy had a _____.

cat nap   pet cat

dog and cat

26

Dad gave Larry a bike. It was red, with tan lines on its sides, and was a nice size for Larry. The bike had big, wide tires for riding in the mud.

Larry liked the bike, but hated riding it in the mud. The bike got muddy, and then he had to wipe it off.

"The bike is too nice," he said to Dad, "I don't want to ride it in the mud."

"It's your bike, so it's up to you," said Dad.

Larry liked riding in the mud.

Larry's bike had red lines on it.

Larry hated riding in the mud.

1, 2, 3, or X?

_____ The vine is big.

_____ Bill had nine dimes.

_____ Bill had ten dimes.

_____ Ann gave a dime to Bill.

1 First

2 Next

3 Then

Paz waves to _____.

safe   lace   Barry

The man will run and _____.

hide   had   pile

Meg said, "The dog is _____ pet."

go   my   by

Rose gave Dan nine _____.

games   tames

hates

Five mice were playing in a wire cage. A big, tan cat came in, put her face up to the cage, and gazed at the mice. She was licking her lips.

"Yikes!" The mice raced to hide. "We can't get out!" they yelled.

Then they saw the wire sides of the cage.

"We can't get out," they said, "but the cat can't get in. We are safe!"

_____

The cat _____ the mice.
       ate   licked   gazed at

The mice were _____.
       yummy   safe   tired

The fuzzy cat hopped up on the side of the tub to see what was inside. But the side of the tub was wet, and she fell in.

"Hiss!!!" The cat jumped out onto the mat.

The sad, soggy cat licked her wet legs. She hated being wet. That was the last time she got onto the tub!

The cat hated getting wet.

The cat liked getting wet.

The cat liked to dive.

1, 2, 3, or X?

____ The hike makes Nam Min tired.

____ Nam Min takes a hike.

____ Nam Min takes a nap.

____ The lime is ripe.

1 First

2 Next

3 Then

Bobby is telling a funny _____ .
joke   jack   bone

The ice _____ is in the cup.
cub   cab   cube

Sen has a big _____ .
rude   use   mule

The man's name is _____ .
Zeke   ten   tune

Dad wanted to sell his van. He got a red pen and made a big FOR SALE note with it. He taped the note to the side of the van.

As Sally rode by on her bike, she saw the note. "Is the van for me, Dad?" said Sally.

Dad patted her on the back. "No," he said. "The note says FOR SALE, not FOR SALLY."

Dad taped a note on the _____.

van   bike   pen

Dad patted Sally's _____.

dog   bike   back

"Look at the robe I got on sale at the mall," says Mom to James, Dave, and Dad, as she takes the robe out of the bag.

She holds it up to James, but he says, "It's too big." Then Mom takes the robe to Dave, but he tells her, "It's too fuzzy for me, Mom."

Dad takes a look at the robe. "Thanks, but it's not my type," he says.

Then Mom puts on the robe. "I think I'll take it," she says. "It fits me fine and I like it."

_____

Mom made a robe for James.

The robe fits Mom.

The robe is size five.

1, 2, 3, or X?

____ The kids hiked a mile up the hill.

____ The tired kids sat on the side of the hill.

____ The kids got tired from hiking.

____ The mice have a nice life.

1 First

2 Next

3 Then

Jenny played _____ Taj.

bone   wipe   with

Kojo hit the bug nine _____.

Tim's   times   pipe

Jack said, "_____ is Pete!"

Cure   Her   Here

The cute black dog has a _____.

woke   bone   cut

Mom was at the lab, and Dad was at home, taking care of Rose. Rose was bored, so she played a joke on Dad. She put on a wig, Mom's robe, and Mom's hat. Then she picked up Mom's bag. She said to Dad, "Hi! I am your wife."

Then Dad kidded Rose. "It's too bad Rose is not here," he said. "We can't play the game I got for her."

"Yes, we can," said Rose. "I'm Rose."

Rose played a joke on _____.

Mom   Dad   the dog

Rose wore Mom's _____.

robe   hose   rose

The puppy likes to dig holes to hide his bones in.

"Mine! All mine!" he says, as he looks at the holes he made in back of the gate.

Then he sees a pile of mud next to a hole in the rose bed. "Did I hide a bone in here?" he says. He pokes his nose into the hole to see, but all he can see is the nose of a mole.

"Get out of my hole!" yells the mole as he jabs the puppy in the nose and dives back into his hole.

The puppy rubs his sore nose. "The holes are not all mine," he says.

The puppy jabs the mole.

The mole has a sore nose.

The puppy and the mole dig holes.

1, 2, 3, or X?

_____ Penny made up a funny joke for the kids.

_____ The kids said, "Tell us a joke."

_____ Dan rode home in a cab.

_____ The kids liked Penny's joke.

1 First

2 Next

3 Then

The _____ is tan.

hope   joke   rope

Ronny said, "Tell _____ a tale."

go   mess   me

The lucky man's name is _____ .

Cube   Luck   Luke

_____ ran out to play.

Eve   here   cuke

Dad was taking a nap. As he dozed, a bug bit him on the nose. Buzz, buzz!

Dad woke up from his nap. As he yelled, he hit at the bug on his nose. Bam, bam!

Dad missed the bug, but he hit his nose. He fumed and rubbed his sore nose. Sob, sob!

Dad hit his _____.

                 bug   leg   nose

Dad missed the _____.

                   bug   kid   man

The man was going to ride the filly for the first time. He got on. At first, the filly hated it, and bucked him off.

But when the man got back on, he rubbed the filly's mane and hummed a tune. She liked him a bit more and let him ride her.

Then the man got off, patted the filly on the neck, and fed her. The filly rubbed the man's back with her nose to tell him she was sorry she bucked him off.

The filly bit the man.

The man tamed the filly.

The man said he was sorry.

1, 2, 3, or X?

____ Paz said, "Yes, I will play."

____ Barry said, "Will you play ball?"

____ Paz and Barry played ball.

____ Mom and Dad are waving.

1 first

2 Next

3 Then

Becky _____ her bike.

woke   rod   rode

Mike has nine _____.

mice   nice   fire

Sally gave a _____ to Bill.

wore   note   not

The van is messy, _____ Patty mops it.

so   sog   by

Wen Lin was dozing in her bed. It was late, but she hated getting up.

Then her kitty came in and hopped up on the bed. The fuzzy cat licked Wen Lin's tired face and woke her up.

Wen Lin hugged the cat and got up out of bed. "I like having you wake me up," she said.

The cat _____ Wen Lin.

dozed on   licked
hugged

Wen Lin _____ the cat.

fed   woke up
hugged

Patty wants to ride her bike to Kate's. "I can't ride my bike," she says. "The back tire has a hole in it."

"I hope I can fix it," she says, and gets the tape. She takes the tire off the bike and tapes up the hole. Then she fills it up. She puts the tire back on the bike and hops on. The tire is fine.

Patty is happy. "I did it!" she yells. "I fixed the bike tire! Now I can ride my bike to Kate's."

Patty rides on the tape.

The tire on the van is ripped.

Patty fixes her bike tire.

1, 2, 3, or X?

____ Bem got a sore leg.

____ Bem likes cake.

____ Bem was riding his bike.

____ Bem fell off the bike.

1 First

2 Next

3 Then

48

The mall is _____.

duke   hug   huge

Nam Min bit on an ice _____.

cube   cub   ride

It's fun to _____ a bike.

dice   rid   ride

Holly is playing _____ ball.

base   bass   fuse

Mom and the kids were at the mall. Zeke saw a juke box and wanted to play it.

"O.K.," said Mom, as she gave him five dimes, "but I hate the tunes you kids play."

Zeke put the dimes into the juke box. "You will like this tune," he said.

Mom did like it. It was an old, jazzy song. She and the kids hummed it.

___

Zeke played the _____.
        game   sax   juke box

Mom _____ the tune.
   hated   played   liked

Rat came to see Mole in his home. Rat sat on a log, got out his pipe, and lit it.

Mole did not look happy. "It's nice to see you," he said, "but you have to go by the rules of my home. We can't have a pipe in here. No, not at all. Smoking is bad for me, and it's bad for you, too."

Mole likes Rat's pipe.

Mole's rule says no pipe.

Rat makes a cute rule.

1, 2, 3, or X?

_____ Red jam got on the tan rug.

_____ Bob wiped up the jam.

_____ Bob's cat tipped the cup of jam.

_____ The dune buggy is huge.

1 First _ _ _ _ _ _ _ _ _ _ _ _ _ _ _ _

_ _ _ _ _ _ _ _ _ _ _ _ _ _ _ _ _ _ _ _

2 Next _ _ _ _ _ _ _ _ _ _ _ _ _ _ _

_ _ _ _ _ _ _ _ _ _ _ _ _ _ _ _ _ _ _ _

3 Then _ _ _ _ _ _ _ _ _ _ _ _ _ _ _

_ _ _ _ _ _ _ _ _ _ _ _ _ _ _ _ _ _ _

A mule looks _____ to a tot.
hug   huge   fume

"We have to go by the _____ ," said Dad.
all   rules   huge

Mom said, "Get an ice _____ ."
fuse   cube   cub

Eve likes her cute pet _____ .
cut   kitty   dune

Bob's van wasn't running. "I'll fix it for you," said Pete.

He gave the van a lube job and a tune up. He put in a fuse and filled up the tires. He wiped off a wet wire and taped up a hole in the gas line.

Pete did a nice job on the van, and it ran well.

"Thank you," said Bob.

Pete wiped the _____.

                  wire   fuse   tire

He put a _____ in the van.

           fuse   hole   pipe

"Let's go," said Zeke, as he gо
kicked the mule in the ribs, but no–
not go.

He hit the mule on the back, but no–
did not go. In a rage, Zeke yelled at the ı
no—the mule did not go.

Zeke gave up and got off the mule. A big ɭ
the mule on the back. That made the mule go!

1, 2,

The mule kicked Zeke.

Zeke made the mule go.

The bug made the mule go.

B, or X?

___ Mom has a huge rope.

___ Paz made a home run.

___ Paz ran to first base.

___ Paz batted the ball.

1 First

2 Next

3 Then

June played on the _____.

dunes   dull   cuke

Taj _____ into the lake.

dives   dice   bite

Dick came _____.

cone   hog   home

The mule is _____.

tan   tuck   duke

As Lilly was getting off the bus, she fell and hit her leg. Her leg wasn't cut, but it was sore. Lilly hopped all the way home.

"Look," Lilly said to Mom.

Mom got her a bag of ice. "Hold the ice on it," said Mom.

Lilly put the ice on her leg. "I fell as I was getting off the bus," she told Mom. "I hit my leg on the side of the bus."

"I did the same thing when I was your age," said Mom, "but when I fell, I got a huge cut on my leg."

_____

Lilly put _____ on her leg.

     socks   ice   tape

Lilly fell off the _____.

     bus   ice box   van

Holly and her dog were running on the dunes. Holly's dog wanted her to toss the rock for him to get, but Holly was tired.

"I'll hide the rock," she said, "so he can't see it." She tossed the rock out into the waves, but her dog saw it. He dived into the waves, picked up the rock, and gave it back to her.

"O.K., I'll play with you," she said.

The dog _____ in the waves.

waved   dived

tossed

Holly wanted to _____ the rock.

hide   saw   kick

1, 2, 3, or X?

_____ The juke box plays a tune for Terry.

_____ Terry puts ten dimes into the juke box.

_____ The hall has a rug in it.

_____ Terry goes up to the juke box.

1 First

2 Next

3 Then

Luke had a _____ to ride.

cube   mud   mule

The kite is _____.

rake   nick   nice

Her _____ is on her face.

nose   not   more

Wen Lin played a _____.

tune   tuck   cuke

It is June, and Mom is out picking her nice, red roses. Her mule is in a pen next to the rose bed. It pokes its nose out of its pen and into Mom's roses.

"No! Get back!" yells Mom. "Roses are not for mules!" But she is too late. The mule takes a huge bite of Mom's rose bed and gets five of the roses.

Mom is fuming. "The rose buds were for putting in a vase, not in your tummy!"

The mule bites the _____.

                              Mom   roses   pen

Mom likes the _____.

                         roses   mule   June

Eve can fix juke boxes and T.V. sets. She goes to the mall to see Miss Jules at the Tune Store.

"I'm looking for a job. I can fix juke boxes and T.V. sets," she tells Miss Jules.

"First I'd like to see if you can fix this juke box. It will not play at all. Then we will see if you can have the job," said Miss Jules.

"I'll take a look," said Eve. Eve fixed the juke box in no time at all, and she got the job.

Eve gets a T.V. set.

Miss Jules hires Eve.

Eve runs the Tune Shop.

1, 2, 3, or X?

_____ The dude rode on the mule.

_____ The dude is rude to Pete.

_____ The dude fell into the mud.

_____ The mule bucked, and the dude fell off.

1 First

2 Next

3 Then

Ice is _____ .

cold   cot   hot

Dick's mom is _____ .

on   old   use

Mike said, "Can you tell _____ the joke?"

me   met   tune

Mom said, " _____ home by five."

Be   bet   dune

"Time for the bike race! Line up!" a man yells to the kids. Betty sees lots of kids with nice bikes, as she lines up her ratty, old bike.

Betty's bike is old, but she likes it.

And they're off! Taj sets the pace, and next comes June on a fine, red bike. But then Betty takes off.

Zip. She passes June.

Zip. She passes Taj.

Zip. She wins the race. Yes, Betty's bike is old, but it is still zippy!

Betty's bike is _____.
nice   old   red

June has a _____ bike.
gold   old   red

"It's my first time at bat. I don't want to miss. I hope I hit the ball. Will I hit a home run?" Jo says in her mind. "Here it goes!"

Bam! Jo hits the ball and runs for her life. The first base man, Sen, has his mitt up to get the ball as she runs to the base.

Sen gets the ball, but he is not on first base. He races back to the base, but Jo tags it first. "Safe!" calls the ref.

"Yes! I did it!" yells Jo.

Jo makes a home run.

Jo is safe on first base.

Jo is out at first base.

1, 2, 3, or X?

_____ Yo and Polly wade in the lake.

_____ Yo and Polly go to the lake.

_____ Yo and Polly go back home with wet legs.

_____ The puppy sits by the wall.

1 First _ _ _ _ _ _ _ _ _ _ _ _ _ _ _

2 Next _ _ _ _ _ _ _ _ _ _ _ _ _

3 Then _ _ _ _ _ _ _ _ _ _ _ _

Pete _____ a joke.

told   here   top

Wen Lin got a _____ from Dad.

dot   bore   box

In June it is not _____.

cold   be   nose

Mom has a nice _____.

more   rob   robe

Mom was carrying Ben at the mall. Kojo came up to see him. "He is getting big," Kojo said to Mom, "and cute, too." Then Kojo waved at Ben and said, "Hi!" Ben waved back, but he said, "Bye-bye."

"I'm not going yet," Kojo told him, rubbing him on the back.

"All he can say is 'bye-bye,' " said Mom. "He can't say 'hi' yet."

"Well, I have to go," said Kojo. Now she waved to Ben and said, "Bye-bye." Then Ben said "Hi" for the first time!

Kojo waved at _____.
        Ben   Mom   Tim

Ben said _____ for the first time.
        "Hi"   "Bye-bye"   "Mom"

June has a sax, but she can't play it. Then she sees a man on T.V. playing the sax.

The man holds the sax up to his lips, so June picks up her sax and puts it up to her lips, too.

The man plays a nice jazz tune on his sax, but June can not play at all. She is sad. Then the man on T.V. says, "You have to play a lot to play well."

June is on T.V.

June plays a nice tune.

June wants to play her sax.

1, 2, 3, or X?

_____ Dot said, "Dad gave me the mule."

_____ The rock ripped the kite.

_____ Eve pinned the rip on the kite.

_____ Eve's kite fell on a rock.

1 First

2 Next

3 Then

Dave rides on the big _____.

mule   pin   pup

Mom can _____ the mat.

cute   gold   fold

Bev has on a gold _____.

lap   pine   pin

Bem's home is by a _____.

my   hi   hill

"I hate being my size," Ricky said to Dad as they got into the van. "I want to be tall like you."

"You will be when you are older," said Dad. "I was your size at your age, too. But being tall is not all fun. I'm so tall I have to have a big bed made for me, and I can't fit into some old homes."

_____

Dad has a _____ made for him.

        van   hot rod   bed

Ricky is _____.

      not tall   tall   riding

The sun is rising in back of the dunes. The tide is up. The waves lap on the rocks. The rising sun makes dotted lines on the lapping waves.

Sun rise is a nice time at the cove. The ducks wade in a line looking for bugs. A gull dips and dives into the waves to get a cod he sees.

The duck finds a cod on the rocks.

The sun is rising on the pike.

The sun is rising at the cove.

1, 2, 3, or X?

_____ Mom says, "Yes, we can."

_____ Missy says, "Can we go to the play?"

_____ Mom uses the pots.

_____ Missy and Mom go to the play.

1 First _ _ _ _ _ _ _ _ _ _ _ _ _ _ _ _

2 Next _ _ _ _ _ _ _ _ _ _ _ _ _ _ _

3 Then _ _ _ _ _ _ _ _ _ _ _ _ _ _

Luke ＿＿＿＿＿＿＿＿ the cat.

holds   tune   hope

Taj ＿＿＿＿＿＿＿＿ the cap for a dime

tube   sock   sold

Polly said, "＿＿＿＿＿＿＿-bye."

Bye   My   At

The fox is ＿＿＿＿＿＿＿.

wild   wind   fold

Dad and the kids are hiking to the lake.

"Are we at the lake yet?" says Eve.

"No, not yet," Dad tells her. They go by big, tall pines.

"Are we at the lake yet?" says Luke.

"No, not yet," Dad tells him. Then they see waves lapping on the rocks.

"It's the lake!" they all yell. "Let's go!"

Dad and the kids go by _____.

                        bikes   pines   lack

They hike to the _____.

               like   lake   dunes

Deke and Paz want to ride bikes to the store, but Deke's bike has a bad tire, so he can't ride it.

"I'm sorry I can't go to the store with you," Deke tells Paz.

"Yes, you can!" says Paz. "Here is the bus. It will get us to the store in no time."

The kids ride bikes to the store.

Deke fixes the hole in his tire.

The kids will take the bus.

1, 2, 3, or X?

_____ The cake fell out of the bag.

_____ The cake made a rip in the bag.

_____ The bus goes by Pam.

_____ Don put the cake in a bag.

1 First ― ― ― ― ― ― ― ― ― ―

2 Next ― ― ― ― ― ― ― ― ―

3 Then ― ― ― ― ― ― ―

80

The nice man was _____ to Ken.

kind   hold   kick

Jack _____ up.

sore   vote   woke

The old man _____ his home.

colt   fold   sold

Rose is telling a funny _____.

joke   jot   hose

Jo Ann was out riding her bike. The puppy wanted to go with her, too. But Jo Ann did not want the puppy to get hit by a bus or a van, so she told him to go home.

"You can't go with me," she said. "Go home!"

The puppy rubbed his nose on Jo Ann's leg and looked up at her with a sad look on his face.

Jo Ann wanted the puppy to be happy, but she wanted him to be safe, too. "No," she said. "You have to go home."

Jo Ann did not want the dog to be _____.

funny   happy   hit

The puppy wanted to _____.

sit   go   hope

A man is at the gate, holding out a roll for the mare and her colt. The old mare is tame, so she goes to get a bite of the roll.

But the colt is wild. He kicks up his hind legs and bolts. Then he puts up his nose and races off.

The colt runs back. He looks at the mare and sees she is safe with the man. Then he goes up to the gate to get a bite, too.

The colt gets a bite of roll.

The colt is not wild.

The colt pokes the man with its nose.

1, 2, 3, or X?

_____ Becky waves at the cab.

_____ The bus is sold.

_____ The cab picks up Becky.

_____ Becky sees a cab.

1 First _____

2 Next _____

3 Then _____

The cat is _____.

cute   jolt   poke

Kojo fell in a _____.

hole   mope   hope

The dog likes _____.

bones   sore   bored

Sally _____ to win.

my   hold   hopes

The kids are making a game at school. It's an old game called Cup and Ball.

First they take a rope. Then they tape a cup to the end of the rope, and they tape a ball to the other end. In the game, they see if they can get the ball into the cup.

_____

The kids make a _____.
                cup   ball   game

The game is called Cup and _____.
                           Ball   Tape   Rope

Taj was wading on the muddy side of the lake.

"Sissy!" Lenny yelled at him. "I dare you to dive in the rocky side of the lake."

Taj didn't want to be called a sissy, but it wasn't safe to dive on the rocky side.

"I don't see you diving on the rocky side, and I'm not calling you names," he told Lenny.

Lenny dares Taj.

Taj takes the dare.

Lenny dives on the rocks.

1, 2, 3, or X?

____ Dad told Bob to get the hose.

____ Dad used the hose on his van.

____ The fox was not wild.

____ Bob got the hose for Dad.

1 First

2 Next

3 Then

Jim has a _____ pin.

we   told   gold

Lin ran _____.

home   hose   rose

Mike _____ up.

woke   wick   lone

Becky is not _____.

home   ham   poke

A cold, wet cat is sitting in the mud by the bus. The cat looks sad. It has no home.

Jo is going by. She sees the cat in the mud and sits by it. "Can I hold you?" she says, and the cat rubs her leg.

"You are a nice cat. I will take you home with me, and you can be my pet," she tells it.

The happy cat licks Jo's face.

The kitty was in the _____.

                             face   mud   sold

Jo _____ the kitty.

      sold   holds   wets

Mom and Dad are fixing up an old bike for Timmy. They are in the hot sun.

"It's all fixed and I am so hot!" said Mom, getting up.

"I'll get you a cup of cold lime ade with lots of ice," said Dad. "And I'll get a cup for me, too."

Dad got lime ade for Mom.

Mom was too cold.

Mom and Dad were fixing a cold bike.

1, 2, 3, or X?

_____ Jim finds a wild cub.

_____ Yoko finds the egg.

_____ Yoko takes a bite of egg.

_____ Mom hides an egg.

1 First _ _ _ _ _ _ _ _ _ _ _ _ _ _

_ _ _ _ _ _ _ _ _ _ _ _ _ _ _ _ _

2 Next _ _ _ _ _ _ _ _ _ _ _ _ _

_ _ _ _ _ _ _ _ _ _ _ _ _ _ _ _ _ _

3 Then _ _ _ _ _ _ _ _ _ _ _ _

_ _ _ _ _ _ _ _ _ _ _ _ _ _ _ _ _ _

Rose is telling a funny _____.

joke   jock   nose

The men _____ home.

go   job   Zeke

The hen got out of its _____.

here   care   cage

Rick said, "_____ puppy is cute."

Be   Me   My

Jo Ann baked a cake for Yo. She made gold icing and put it on the cake. Then she put Yo's name on the cake with red icing. Jo Ann gave the cake to Yo.

"Thank you," he said. "The cake looks yummy, and I like the icing."

Jo Ann made ＿＿＿＿＿＿＿ icing.

        red   gold   hot

Yo said he liked the ＿＿＿＿＿＿＿.

        cake   icing   cone

Luke and his dad ride bikes to the mall. Luke sees a gold yo-yo he likes for 90¢. "I have nine dimes," he tells his dad, "but they are in my bike bag. I'll be back."

"O.K.," says Dad. "I'll be here by the juke box."

Luke gets the dimes and goes back to get the yo-yo, but it's not in the case.

"I'm sorry," says the man in the mall. "I sold the gold yo-yo."

Luke is sad, but then he sees Dad holding the yo-yo.

Luke sold the gold yo-yo.

Dad gets the yo-yo for Luke.

Luke has five dimes.

1, 2, 3, or X?

_____ Tom gave the rose bud to Yoko.

_____ Tom picked a rose bud.

_____ Harry folded a play jet.

_____ Yoko liked getting the rose bud.

1 First

2 Next

3 Then